THE HOUSE PONY

AN ABC OF HORSEMANSHIP

JULIET BLAXLAND

J.A. ALLEN

Introduction

This is the story of a pony who was found wandering about on the M4 motorway, and then found himself in the care of a kind and knowledgeable horsey person, who we shall call Aunt Jelly. Aunt Jelly was a scatterbrain about everything except horses. Aunt Jelly lived in a big, crumbling house in the country, and looked after a large number of animals that had been sent to her by people who had rescued them from various cruelties. Aunt Jelly also had a scruffy tomboy niece called Tuttyhead who, for reasons too boring to explain, was staying with her for a long holiday. Tuttyhead wanted the motorway pony to be allowed to live in the house.

'Please may the motorway pony come and live in the house, Aunt Jelly?' asked Tuttyhead.

'Of course he can. He can live in the house and be known as The House Pony, but you must look after him, and see to all his needs, and make sure he is happy. It will be fun!' said Aunt Jelly, with a look that hinted that the last place a pony should live is in a house.

Oh my giddy aunt, thought Tuttyhead. Anyone else's aunt would have said no to the idea of The House Pony. The needs and wants of a real live pony suddenly seemed a big responsibility. The House Pony himself also seemed suddenly quite big.

'Right. Let's start,' said Aunt Jelly. So they did.

A

'The first rule of keeping animals,' said Aunt Jelly, 'is Animals First, meaning that their needs come before ours.' Aunt Jelly certainly practised what she preached. A large greyhound, Chuffy, and a small fuzzy dog, Agog, slept on a sofa while The House Pony clomped about the house. Tuttyhead began to fret about his needs.

What a pony needs most is fresh air, exercise, food, water and shelter. A pony in the wild lives in a herd, in open country where he can look out for any animals who might want to attack and eat him (predators). Being in an enclosed space with a roof is unnatural to horses.

B

The House Pony explored the house and lay down on a four-poster bed. Tuttyhead could immediately see that what might be luxury to a human or a dog, does not necessarily meet the needs of a pony. Aunt Jelly believed in learning from practical real life action, not from books.

Horse bedding may be straw, wood shavings or pellets, shredded paper or cardboard, hemp, etc. Horses can sleep standing up. A group of horses outdoors will often take turns to stand guard while others sleep. It is sensible to budget realistically, avoiding wasting money on gimmicks.

C

One of the first problems of keeping
The House Pony as a house pony was that he
neighed very loudly as he clomped about the
house. Tuttyhead correctly imagined that The
House Pony might be lonely, calling out for his
herd and his ancestors, so she resolved to find
him a suitable friend.

*Horses and ponies are herd animals who need company.
On the other hand, any animal can become a friend. Stories
abound of smart racehorses who have become inseparable
from their companion goats or sheep. The overall shape of
a horse or pony, his form, is known as his conformation (not
confirmation). Good conformation helps a pony move and
balance himself well.*

D

The needs and wants of The House Pony came thick and fast, but Tuttyhead was a tidy tomboy so she put them roughly into alphabetical order in her head. Freedom from disease, discomfort or distress, were among the most basic needs of The House Pony, and Tuttyhead added dentist and dun under D, just to be thorough. The House Pony's colour was dun with a dorsal stripe down his back.

Horses and ponies are descended from ancient animals about the size of a dog, and used to have five toes on each foot, but the central toe gradually evolved into a single hoof.
On the inside of a horse's leg there is a little growth known as the chestnut, which is the 'dinosaur memory' of his ancient ancestors' original toes. Sometimes horses need a visit from an equine dentist. Dun is a colour that carries memories of prehistoric horse genes, often with black points and markings.

E

Tuttyhead put a headcollar on The House Pony and led him outside to search for a suitable friend. In a small paddock near the kitchen lived a young Exmoor pony called Mousie, an old donkey called Oaty, and an even older little grey pony called Merrilegs.

Horses, ponies, mules, donkeys and zebras are all EQUINES. The n horse, Equus caballus, belongs to the family Equidae, which includes asses and zebras. Equus is the Latin root word of equitation (riding) and equestrian (rider, or relating to riding). Caballus is the Latin root word of cavalry (e.g. The Household Cavalry). Equine grass sickness (EGS) is a sometimes fatal illness, which is related to eating too much rich grass, although the exact cause is unknown.

Aunt Jelly was keen on quoting from 'The Nine Golded Rules of Feeding'. Aunt Jelly tested Tuttyhead on these rules, but in reality the main rule seemed to be not to overfeed either the horse or the rider, as in, 'F is for FAT'. The House Pony raided the kitchen for food, but Aunt Jelly did not notice, because she never spent much time in the kitchen, or thought much about food at all.

Animals have a right, in law, to 'The Five Freedoms' (see W for Welfare). Access to a suitable diet and water is one of the most basic needs of any animal. A pony's natural way of eating is to graze, eating little and often, but it can be as cruel to allow a pony to eat too much, and become obese, as to let him be hungry.
A horse's natural defences in the wild are fight or flight.

G

The House Pony had shed his hairs all over the four-poster bed, so Tuttyhead decided to groom him for what seemed like hours, brushing his coat and his mane and tail, sponging his nostrils, picking out his feet and oiling his neat little unshod hooves. Grooming was a calming, bonding ritual. Tuttyhead and The House Pony found a pleasing relaxation in each other's company.

In the wild and in the field, horses and ponies enjoy mutual grooming, which reinforces social bonds and hierarchies. Grooming a pony, including checking him over and picking out his feet, will increase his trust and enjoyment of people, and keep his coat glossy, and free of scurf and dead hairs.

H

One thing Aunt Jelly was fond of saying was, 'No foot, no 'oss.' What she meant is that it is essential to look after a horse's hooves, to pick them out with a hoof pick to keep them clean, and to have them regularly trimmed and/or shod by a qualified farrier. By the time Tuttyhead had finished oiling his hooves, The House Pony looked ready for the smartest of events requiring 'smart turnout'.

If you do not look after a horse's feet, your horse will be lame (no foot) and will not be able to do the normal work of being a horse, such as being ridden (no 'oss). As part of the exam to qualify as a farrier, a farrier has to make all sorts of shapes of shoe, from scratch, from a straight iron bar.

I

Horses and ponies will find ways to injure themselves, no matter how much we do to protect them. Aunt Jelly was of the opinion that ignorance is no excuse for cruelty, even if it is unintentional, so, along with 'the bobbery pack' of her different-sized dogs, she took Tuttyhead and The House Pony with her as she did the rounds, checking all the horses and ponies in her care. Aunt Jelly's conversation was a constant broadcast of practical pony-care advice, pointing out hazards, dropping little nuggets of knowledge, nudging Tuttyhead to see the world from a pony's point of view.

In the wild, an injured pony might become isolated from the herd, making him vulnerable to predators. A modern pony's natural instincts are still programmed to protect him from being attacked by an imaginary lion. Ironically, the instinctive fear of injury triggers the flight response, which often leads to injury.

J

As Aunt Jelly, Tuttyhead and the dogs did the rounds, The House Pony met all sorts of strange new sights, large and noisy farm machinery, etc. But it was the sight of his own reflection in a puddle that made him jump out of his skin – not literally, but enough that he jumped a big hedge.

Ponies are natural jumpers, but can be spooked by the smallest obstacle. Ponies can also be accident-prone. It is wise for all horse owners to have a Just-in-Case Plan, to think ahead for what might happen, and what will happen, and what to do at the end of the horse or pony's life.

K

The House Pony had accidentally jumped into a field where some ponies were eating out of buckets. His unexpected arrival caused an outbreak of jealousy: ears back, threats of kicking, silent communication. Aunt Jelly always added an extra bucket so that the meekest could eat. The House Pony stuck his nose in the spare bucket, so he was very easy to catch. Later, with The House Pony in the kitchen, Aunt Jelly showed Tuttyhead how to tie a quick-release safety knot on the Aga rail.

Kicking is one of the natural defences of all horses when threatened in the wild, and also reinforces herd hierarchies. A zebra crossing a river in Africa can kill a crocodile with a kick. It is sensible when feeding ponies in a field to allow one more bucket or heap of hay than the number of ponies being fed, and it is also sensible to keep a tight rein on kit, avoiding expensive unnecessaries.

L

The ponies with the buckets had for various reasons come to Aunt Jelly too thin, but other ponies were on limited rations for their own good. The House Pony was not too thin. He had been tethered on a grass verge next to the motorway, with lorries roaring past, and an old loo for a water bucket.

Lameness has many causes, one of which is Laminitis, a disease of the hoof (not the leg). Limiting access to rich grass can help prevent Laminitis, as it often affects small ponies who are too fat.

M

The House Pony was of unknown breeding, but was probably a mixture of British mountain and moorland breeds. For centuries, his pony-ancestors had been brave, hardy and hard-working, so he had been unafraid of motorway juggernauts, and had kept himself fit by walking in circles, the instincts to graze and move being stronger than his desire to escape. His owner had died of old age.

Monitoring a pony's muscle tone, movement and weight is a natural part of good horsemanship and the daily routine. In the wild, horse and ponies are constantly on the move in search of new grazing. Exmoor ponies have oat-coloured noses, or 'mealy mouths'.

N

Through the kitchen window, The House Pony watched with head held high and ears all pricked as two horses were play-fighting. Another pony was rolling. Most of the horses just grazed quietly.

It is enshrined in law that animals should have 'freedom to exhibit normal behaviour'. In the case of horses and ponies, this would include freedom to move around, lie down, engage with other horses, and sometimes to roll. The Household Cavalry horses, who live in London for ceremonial duties, go on a holiday every summer, where they live a more natural life and swim in the sea.

The House Pony clomped around the kitchen and pushed his nose into what looked like a big orange bucket on the table. There was a monster in the 'bucket', and it fell to the floor with an almighty crash, giving The House Pony a terrible fright as he fled outdoors and into the garden.

Outdoors is the natural place for horses and ponies, who can become bored in a stable. Occupying a horse in a stable can be achieved with toys, mirrors, other horses nearby, etc., depending on the character of each horse. Over-breeding, in the sense of breeding too many foals, is self-regulating in the truly wild state, but in the modern human world, it is the responsibility of owners not to breed unwanted foals. Owners of every single horse and pony would ideally be traceable on a database, registered and with an owner held responsible at every stage of life, from birth to death.

P

Tuttyhead was horrified. Poor Little Terrified House Pony! Aunt Jelly chuckled quietly to herself at this predictable predicament, a little fiasco that was easy to see coming if you understood a little bit about how a pony thinks. Outside, The House Pony was already calmly munching something green in the kitchen garden. Aunt Jelly expected this too, and luckily she wasn't fussy about gardening.

Ponies are easily spooked, but peace is usually quickly restored. Pony psychology says 'run!' at the slightest spook. The source can be investigated after survival! Prevention of pain, fear, accident, injury and other potential disasters can often be helped by trying to understand the psychology of the horse, to foresee the foreseeable, to think like a pony.

Questions, questions, questions. Tuttyhead asked endless questions in her head about The House Pony. Would he like a drink of water? What would he like to do? Is he lonely? What does he need? It was a clever wheeze by Aunt Jelly, to say yes to the idea that The House Pony could live in the house on condition that Tuttyhead was responsible for his needs. One morning of questions had taught Tuttyhead more about thinking like a pony than a month of someone else doing it all for her would have done, or reading about pony care in a dry old book with 'Horsemanship' in the title.

The Queen loves horses, especially her own racehorses, and some of them travel across the world. Quarantine separates horses and ponies from others who may have a disease, and prevents illnesses spreading. The quagga was an equine animal like a half-stripey zebra, now sadly extinct.

R

Tuttyhead and The House Pony were admiring a wall of rosettes when Aunt Jelly's voice suddenly bellowed as if from several fields away: 'RAGWORT!' Tuttyhead and The House Pony trotted over to find Aunt Jelly attacking a bright yellow flower, cursing as she dug it out by its roots, and explaining how poisonous it was to ponies, especially if accidentally dried into hay.

Ragwort (Jacobaea vulgaris) is a very common yellow wild flower, which causes liver failure in horses and ponies. A cumulative effect can eventually lead to blindness. It is essential that horse owners recognize this plant at all stages of its growth, and remove it by digging it out by its roots and burning it. Contact with ragwort makes some people ill, so it is sensible to wear gloves.

S

Tuttyhead and The House Pony were getting on like a house on fire, or more accurately a house not on fire, so Tuttyhead put on a riding hat from the tack room, and without any drama, vaulted onto The House Pony, bareback, with a headcollar, but without a saddle or bridle. Conventional pony textbooks might advise more caution, but this was a real pony, in real life, and it seemed natural.

Riding without a saddle is a good way of learning to ride by 'feel' not by numbers. It is almost impossible not to sit properly without a saddle or stirrups. Riding by 'feel' also naturally makes it easy for the rider to put themselves in the position of the horse, and therefore to question conventions such as keeping horses and ponies in a stable all day, when they might prefer a field.

The House Pony was a bold pony by nature, so he was not at all bothered by having such a lightweight person riding him. Besides, unknown to Tuttyhead, Aunt Jelly knew that The House Pony had been ridden before. Aunt Jelly had started teaching Tuttyhead to ride, on a very small and docile 'dog pony' called Dynamite, long before Tuttyhead could walk. Tuttyhead and The House Pony went on a little explore, and came back warmer and happier from the exercise.

Horses and ponies need fresh air and exercise, and temperature is naturally self-regulating. Modern rugs for horses have evolved more than any other item of tack, but have also become an item of fashion. Horses and ponies normally need rugs only if we remove their hair, by clipping them, for high-performance exercise such as racing and eventing. Hairy ponies do not need rugs, and over-heating a pony by over-rugging can be cruel. All animals need shade from the sun.

U

Understanding a pony's thoughts, or trying to, was intriguing to Tuttyhead, and The House Pony seemed to have no trouble communicating his needs and opinions. He wasn't at all afraid of big horses or big dogs or tractors or lorries, but jumped (literally) at the sight of himself in a puddle.

Understanding the nature of horses and ponies makes it easier to tell when something is wrong, and what might be wrong. Changes in behaviour could be caused by pain or discomfort, teeth, back problems, boredom from being kept in stable with nothing to do, loneliness, etc.

V

A muddy Land Rover, apparently held together with black tape, screeched to a halt. The vet had arrived to examine some ponies, including The House Pony. The vet talked to the ponies as he looked at their teeth and felt their legs. The vet said The House Pony was about seven years old, with 'his best years ahead of him'. Aunt Jelly and the vet exchanged technical-sounding opinions, mostly about vaccinations and stable vices caused by boredom. Tuttyhead watched and listened.

In old horse books, vices were written about rather melodramatically, as if a horse had a reasoned desire to be mean, and included behaviour like rearing, bucking and bolting. In modern language, the word 'vices' usually refers to anxiety or boredom-related tics that are difficult to cure, behaviour like weaving and wind-sucking, which legally must be mentioned if a horse is sold.

W

The vet roared off, and Tuttyhead wondered if The House Pony would like a drink, so she led him up the stairs and into a bathroom. Tuttyhead filled the bath up with water, and led The House Pony to it. The House Pony had a good look at the bath, and splashed water everywhere with his nose, but did not want a drink. Tuttyhead learnt first-hand what our ancestors have been telling us for centuries: You can lead a house pony to a bath full of water, but you can't make him drink.

Horses and ponies need unrestricted access to clean water, with regular stops for water if travelling. In the past, horses and ponies were routinely 'wormed', (given medicine to prevent worms), but this is now done only when necessary, otherwise animals develop a resistance that can stop common medicines being effective any more. In modern life it is likely that weight (i.e. being overweight, being obese, being too fat) is a more common health problem, in both horse and rider.

X

Tuttyhead was a bit worn out with thinking about the needs of The House Pony, and wondered if Aunt Jelly was thinking at all about the needs of Tuttyhead. It turned out she was. Aunt Jelly had made an enormous green salad of the green stuff in the kitchen garden, for all three of them to have for supper. She also gave Tuttyhead a beautiful, serious, tatty old book with 'Horsemanship' in the title. Aunt Jelly, Tuttyhead and The House Pony munched their greens and studied the book.

For horses and ponies, like people, xxx love is not all you need. Horses and ponies need fresh air and exercise, water, shelter, the right food but not too much of it, and people who understand their needs. Aunt Jelly was a wise old bird in this respect, and knew exactly what she was doing when she indulged Tuttyhead's idea of The House Pony. She had taught Tuttyhead to think like a pony.

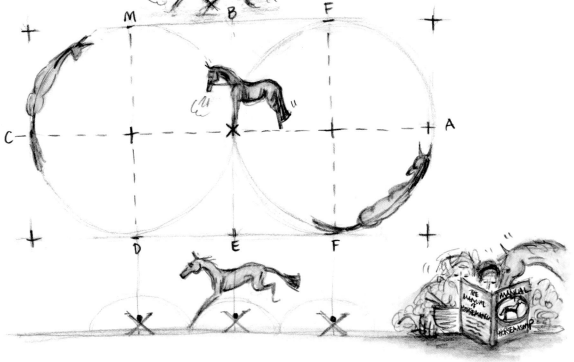

Y

By now it was late-ish, so Aunt Jelly took the dogs, Tuttyhead and The House Pony to do the final walk-round of her tidy yard. Most of the horses would spend the night turned out in fields, with only the old grey pony, Merrilegs, in a stable, awaiting a special visit first thing in the morning. Aunt Jelly asked Tuttyhead if The House Pony should sleep in the house, or outside in the paddock near the kitchen door, with the mealy-mouthed Exmoor pony, Mousie, and the old donkey, Oaty.

Tuttyhead thought, and said, 'Outside'.

'That is the right answer,' said Aunt Jelly.

And it was.

'Yard Discipline' is an old-fashioned phrase, visible in practice in any reputable horsey place. Yards will be swept, muck heaps tidy, water buckets full and clean, tack rooms immaculate. Equines of all sorts have an average natural lifespan of about thirty years, so there are about three pony years to one human year. A pony is 'in his prime' from the ages of eight to fourteen years. The age of a pony can be judged by looking at his teeth, which is the origin of the phrase 'long in the tooth', meaning old.

Z

Aunt Jelly and Tuttyhead turned The House Pony out in the paddock with his new friends Moorland Mousie and Donkey Oaty (where he had happily spent the past three weeks, although Tuttyhead did not know this). These three happy little companions confounded the old cliché says that says two's company but three's a crowd. Perhaps dear old Merrilegs had balanced their world. Aunt Jelly said goodnight to the ponies, and Oaty, with an especially long goodnight to Merrilegs in her stable. Once the bobbery pack had 'done everything', Aunt Jelly and Tuttyhead returned to the house...

Not much later, Tuttyhead and the dogs went to sleep.

It had been rather tiring for Tuttyhead, trying to think like a pony all day...

And then dreaming about thinking like a pony all night...

Zzz...

Aunt Jelly poured herself a glass of Good Ordinary Claret, and pondered over the lessons Tuttyhead had learned that day: that a pony is not a dog; that keeping a pony in the house does not meet his real-life needs; that a pony has his own individual likes and dislikes; that you can lead a horse to water but you can't make it drink. The dogs snored, but Aunt Jelly did not want to go to sleep that night, because then too soon it would be the morning. Aunt Jelly believed it was her duty to give all animals in her care a good life, and a good death. And she practised what she preached.

'Goodnight, Merrilegs,' whispered Aunt Jelly to the oblivious dogs.

'Goodnight, little ponio.'

Zzz…

About 90 per cent of equines in the world are working equines, e.g. used for transport or carrying loads.

'Equine euthanasia', humanely putting a horse down for its own welfare, is resisted in some cultures,

but with domestication came the responsibility for us to provide a good death for our animals.

Euthanasia must be taught as the compassionate way to end an animal's life.

And finally…

The House Pony never had a proper name.

Perhaps you can think of a good name for him.

Dun-something?

Real-life House Ponies

Fairy Violet Crème (Shetland pony), owned by Lord De La Warr (2016). 'Fairy' is the stud prefix of the South Park Shetland Pony Stud, which is the oldest of all Shetland pony studs, and is currently owned by Lady De La Warr. Its stud books date back to the 1870s and are kept at the Dorset Arms pub in Withyham, Sussex, on the Buckhurst Park estate belonging to the Earl De La Warr. Fairy Violet Crème was photographed in the Dorset Arms for *Tatler* magazine. Queen Victoria had two ponies from the stud.

Moti (grey pony) – owned by Penelope Betjeman, a regular indoor tea guest (1930s). Moti has been described as the centre of Penelope Betjeman's life and the third person in her marriage. A very white 'grey', Moti had been Penelope Betjeman's hunter with the Delhi Foxhounds, and was shipped back to England from India. The name Moti is Hindi for 'pearl'. There are several famous photographs of Moti indoors, standing calmly while being painted or having tea in formal rooms, with Penelope Betjeman, Lord Berners and others, at Faringdon House, appropriately just beneath the White Horse of Uffington.

A Horsey Alphabet

(Chosen for broad historical interest, and worth a google on a rainy day)

A   Arkle, steeplechaser; Aldiniti, steeplechaser

B   Badminton, horse trials; Burmese, ceremonial horse; *Black Beauty*, book by Anna Sewell

C   Copenhagen, cavalry horse, charger of the Duke of Wellington at Waterloo

D   Devon Loch, steeplechaser; Desert Orchid, steeplechaser

E   Eclipse, flat racehorse, and eighteenth-century stallion from which nearly all modern racehorses are descended

F   Foinavon, steeplechaser and Grand National fence; Frankel, Flat racehorse

G   'Golden Gorse', author of *Moorland Mousie* (1929); Golden Miller, steeplechaser

H   Hippo, Ancient Greek for horse (Hippopotamus, 'river horse')

I   Irish Draught, horse breed, basis of Household Cavalry horses, Cavalry Blacks

J   Joey, fictional horse in *War Horse*, book/play/film by Michael Morpurgo

K   Killaire, eventer, (see also Badminton); Kauto Star, steeplechaser

L   Lipizzaner, horse breed, the 'white horses' of the Spanish Riding School of Vienna

M   Munnings, Sir Alfred, horse artist and sculptor; Milton, showjumper, won £1 million

N   Newmarket, known as 'HQ', historical centre of British racing for 300 years

O   OTTB, 'off-track Thoroughbred', American/Australian term for ex-racehorses

P   Pullein-Thompson sisters, authors of pony books; Lucinda Prior-Palmer, eventer

Q   Quagga, extinct equine; *The Queen's Cavalry*, film about training the Household Cavalry

R   Red Rum, steeplechaser, legendary three times winner of the Grand National

S   Stubbs, George, horse artist and recorder/author of *The Anatomy of the Horse*

T   Tattersalls, traditional auctioneers of racehorses

U   *Up, Up and Away, the biography of Be Fair*, book by Lucinda Green (Prior-Palmer)

V   Valegro, dressage horse; Vale of the White Horse (see also White Horse of Uffington)

W   Whistlejacket, Marquess of Rockingham's racehorse, lifesize painting by Stubbs (1762)

X   Xenophon (c.430–354 BC), Ancient Greek cavalry officer, author of *On Horsemanship*

Y   Yearling, a horse between twelve and twenty-four-months-old; yew, a tree and hedge plant poisonous to horses

Z   Zebra, three species and several subspecies, all uniquely striped (*Hippotigris*, 'stripey horse')

The Animal Welfare Act (2006) enshrines in law the following 'five freedoms':

◡ Freedom to live in a suitable environment

◡ Freedom to have access to a suitable diet and water

◡ Freedom to exhibit normal behaviour patterns

◡ Freedom to be housed with, or apart from, other animals

◡ Freedom to be protected from pain, suffering, injury and disease